CLOUD STUDIES IN COLOUR

CUMULUS OVER MOUNTAINS

Cumulus forms predominantly over the higher ground because the heat source is at a higher level and the air temperature is higher than at the same altitude over the low ground. Anabatic winds serve to maintain this situation by feeding the heat conveyed into the air over the valleys into the bases of the cumulus over the mountains (see **55**). Over the valleys the subsidence at cloud levels produces the sub-cloud inversion (see **47**) which prevents thermals from reaching the condensation level there.

Glaciation can be clearly seen in the silkiness of the growing anvil on the left and in the fibrous top in the distance on the right. This might be due to the towers reaching a level where it is as cold as −40°C, or the glaciation might be occurring at lower levels in older parts of the cloud where some droplets had grown to drizzle size and therefore freeze more readily at higher temperatures than −40°C. However in clouds such as these, with strong upcurrents (contrast with **17**), the glaciation probably occurs near to −40°C. So long as the thermal is strong inside a rising tower, it retains its sharply outlined form even when glaciated; but the glaciation becomes immediately apparent in the cloud texture as soon as the upcurrent ceases.

The cloud base is at a uniform height, which is the result of the layer below being well mixed and the evaporation being rather small in this desert country.

CLOUD STUDIES
IN COLOUR

BY

RICHARD SCORER
Professor of Theoretical Mechanics at Imperial College, London

AND THE LATE
HARRY WEXLER
Formerly Director of Research United States Weather Bureau, Washington

PERGAMON PRESS
OXFORD · LONDON · EDINBURGH · NEW YORK
TORONTO · SYDNEY · PARIS · BRAUNSCHWEIG

Pergamon Press Ltd., Headington Hill Hall, Oxford
4 & 5 Fitzroy Square, London W.1

Pergamon Press (Scotland) Ltd., 2 & 3 Teviot Place, Edinburgh 1

Pergamon Press Inc., 44-01 21st Street, Long Island City, New York 11101

Pergamon of Canada Ltd., 6 Adelaide Street East, Toronto, Ontario

Pergamon Press (Aust.) Pty. Ltd.
Rushcutters Bay, Sydney, New South Wales

Pergamon Press S.A.R.L., 24 rue des Écoles, Paris 5^e

Vieweg & Sohn GmbH, Burgplatz 1, Braunschweig

Printed in Great Britain by The Nuffield Press Ltd., Cowley, Oxford

08 202696 3

68/ 6992

CONTENTS

ACKNOWLEDGMENTS

THE authors wish to thank the following for permission to use their photographs

HAROLD KLIEFORTH — Frontispiece, 71, 79, Steep wave (p.XI)

N. D. P. HUGHES — 14

BETSY WOODWARD — 19, 21, 33

Shell International Petroleum Co. Ltd. (Photo by J. R. WESKE) — 73

E. HESSTVEDT and H. G. HEMM — 76

F. H. LUDLAM — 102, Hailstones (p.XII)

G. L. STOLLERY — 112

HANS NEUBERGER — 114

MILAN KOLDOVSKY — 121, Behind a cold Front (p.XI)

D. M. COOKSON — Scud, Thermal Upcurrents

H. T. B. KETTLEWELL — Alto-stratocumulus (p.IX)

GEORGE THOMPSON — Motion of Waves

G. E. STONE — Cooling Towers (cover)

The other photographs were taken by R. S. SCORER.

LEGENDS FOR COVER ILLUSTRATIONS

1. On a calm morning or evening the lowest layers of air are cooler, moister, and hazier; and when the sun is close to the horizon its image is distorted by refraction of the rays as they pass at a glancing angle through these layers. At this time, but not at other times because of the danger of eye damage, binoculars may be used to see sunspots: two are visible in this picture, which was taken across the sea from Karachi in winter.

2. Thunder clouds grow more readily over mountains because the sun's heat is communicated from the ground to the atmosphere at a higher altitude there. When they reach up to the base of the stratosphere they are not buoyant enough to rise further, and so they spread out like hot air on the ceiling. The very vigorous cloud on the left penetrated temporarily into the stratosphere but soon afterwards had sunk down again.

These clouds were formed over the Pyrenees in a flood of cool air which had moved southwards across France in August. This air drained southwards into the Mediterranean, causing the Mistral to blow through the mountain gaps.

3. In air moving across a coast on to warm ground on a sunny day, convection currents are produced which become visible as cumulus clouds. They are bright white as they grow upwards and then become darker as they evaporate. This is a summer photograph on the coast of Wales.

4. The heat from the cooling towers and chimneys of this power station, situated between Coventry and Birmingham, produces a convection current with a cumulus cloud at the top. The cloud is visible at a lower level than natural clouds because of the added moisture from the cooling towers.

5. The bending of the sun's rays in the air which is colder near the ground makes the sun's lower edge appear to be higher than it really is, and so it appears flattened.

Because of its apparent proximity to the trees the sun also appears to be larger when it is near the horizon, but this is an illusion: in fact its apparent area is smaller because of the flattening.

6. Close to the equator showers are frequent over the ocean at all times of year. The sea is warm and the air from higher latitudes is 'boiled up' into tall cumulus. Rainbows are common morning and evening, the winds are generally light, and the dense white clouds cast dark shadows when seen against the sun. This picture was taken over the Indian Ocean about 1000 miles east of Mogadiscio in August.

7. Rainbows are best seen in the evening when the sun is low and shines on the rain which is not shaded by the clouds from which it is falling, and consequently low arcs such as this one are rare. But downwind of mountains there are often clear gaps through which the sun shines, and in this case the drizzly rain was being produced continuously over the mountain so that it was still falling through the air under the clear space. The bow was visible one late August morning for about 40 minutes over Ullswater.

The bow is clearly seen as the coloured edge of the region from which white sunlight is reflected back to the observer. Outside the arc the rain is scarcely visible and the sky is therefore darker.

PREFACE

1. LUKE HOWARD—"*On the modification of clouds and on the principles of their production, suspension, and destruction.*" J. Taylor (London 1803).

2. W. CLEMENT LEY—*Cloudland* Edward Stanford (London 1894).

3. SIR NAPIER SHAW—*Manual of Meteorology* Vols 1-4, C. U. Press 1926-31.

4. ARTHUR W. CLAYDEN—*Cloud Studies* John Murray 1905.

5. *International Cloud Atlas*—World Meteorological Organisation 1956.
6. *Cloud Types for Observers*—Meteorological Office 717; H.M.S.O. 1962.

7. G. A. CLARKE—*Clouds* Constable 1920, and C. J. P. CAVE—*Clouds* C. U. Press 1926.

8. MANFRED CURRY—*Cloud, Wind, and Water* Country Life 1951.
9. W. J. HUMPHREYS—*Fogs and Clouds* Waverley Press (Baltimore) 1926.

NAMES for cloud forms were first successfully proposed by Luke Howard[1] in 1803. He recognised three distinct forms—cirrus, cumulus, and stratus—and he tried to describe all forms in terms of these three. He equated nimbus, the rain cloud, with cirro-cumulo-stratus. This neat arrangement, consisting of seven possible forms was excellent. It was not so complicated that it could be twisted to suit any situation, nor too simple for the understanding of the time. It enabled people to think coherently about clouds.

The next notable record of advance was made by Clement Ley,[2] who was an assiduous watcher of the sky. By 1877 he had recognised the dimensions of a cyclone and even saw that the circulation was further to the west at a higher level. Unfortunately he proliferated the Latin nomenclature and gave some rather fanciful explanations. Howard, of course, had tried to explain cloud forms and had made great play with the idea of electric forces; but not until the thermodynamics had been put on a sound basis by Napier Shaw[3] and others was it possible for correct explanations to begin to be found. Even Shaw's classic "when the condensation of vapour is continued beyond the limit of the carrying power of cloud, rain is formed" is scarcely an explanation, and it was necessary to wait for the full development of aviation for the science of cloud study to be properly established. Meanwhile three things had been going on. Observers, following in the tradition of Ley, notably Arthur Clayden,[4] were accumulating knowledge by their alertness, by photography (including measurements in three dimensions by two cameras) and by sound physical thinking. Most of the main cloud types were fairly well understood by Clayden by 1922. But with the development of weather services the need for a coded form for cloud observations had forced the thinking of the majority of meteorologists along the all too familiar lines of low, medium and high clouds, with the prefixes alto- and cirro- to denote these last two categories. At the same time Howard's use of Latin names, and the elaboration of them by Ley and others, seems to have precipitated meteorologists into a Linnean system of genera and species which, however appropriate for flora, products of evolution, is quite ridiculous for clouds. Unfortunately this habit of mind still lingers and the classification which has resulted is still the official one. [5,6]

The attention of the majority of meteorologists has been channelled, by the demand for forecasting services, into the drawing of charts and the study of the large scale processes of weather development which can only be seen in toto on charts. As far as clouds were concerned they were content with the general physical principles outlined by Shaw. But the attention of a minority was still on the weather as it can be seen by the solitary observer. Outstanding among those who collected photographic records of cloud forms are G. A. Clarke[7] and C. J. P. Cave.[7] But even they appear to have been content with the rather obvious kinds of explanation already well known. Although they contributed outstanding collections of pictures their contributions to the thinking was small compared with the advances made by Ley and Clayden. Many writers since then have published fine illustrations of clouds with the "usual explanations"; some have even faked very dramatic pictures.[8]

It remained to W. J. Humphreys[9] to continue where Shaw left off. He combined the understanding of one of the world's leading meteorological physicists with the keen eye of the best of field observers. Many details which had passed

10. W. J. Humphreys— *Physics of the Air* Part IV, McGraw Hill, New York, 1920, for which credit is due to E. W. Woolard.

11. Ann Douglas—*Cloud Reading for Pilots* John Murray 1943.

12. F. H. Ludlam and R. S. Scorer—*Cloud Study* John Murray (London) 1957.

unnoticed by Clarke and Cave attracted his attention. For example the pileus cloud, prominently illustrated by Howard, seems to have been forgotten or confused with the ice anvil until Humphreys correctly explained it, calling it the scarf cloud. He was not a slave to the use of the Latin names. Also in Humphreys' *Physics of the Air* [10] we find the best treatment of optical phenomena.

Because of their preoccupation with isobars meteorologists do not come as much into contact with glider pilots as they should, and it is a sad commentary on their interests that it was left to an amateur meteorologist, Ann Douglas, to produce the first book [11] on clouds for glider pilots. Her writing reveals an emancipation from the clutter of the orthodox terminology, and an overwhelming concern to understand how clouds behave rather than to fit them into a preconceived scheme. Ludlam and Scorer [12] followed this precedent and completely ignored the international classification in their arrangement. They used the terminology only so far as it suited their purpose.

It seemed that certain tasks remained to be done. The first was to make available as comprehensive a collection of cloud pictures in colour as possible. The second was to reduce to a minimum the Latin names and only use well-known ones. When additions were required English words should be used, according to the practice of mathematicians and physicists rather than that of botanists and zoologists. In compiling Part I of our book we have tried to exemplify all the common cloud forms. This is now published separately and is written as concisely as possible in order that it may be used as a practical work of reference. It is assumed that the reader will refer to other books for a fuller description of the well-known meteorological processes. In Part II we have examined clouds in much greater detail, added additional studies of smoke clouds, aircraft condensation trails, and TIROS photographs, and given pictures of numerous less common, more violent, and more spectacular phenomena. Parts I and II together comprise our "Colour Encyclopaedia of Clouds".

No two clouds are identical, and we are conscious that forms will be observed by readers which we have omitted: while we hope that most of the explanations will be found somewhere among those given here, we also know that keen observers will see in a few years as many new forms again as we have given, and will probe in greater detail and with deeper understanding into those processes which we have only described qualitatively.

We are grateful to all those people, organisations, and departments who have so readily made their pictures available for inclusion, and we acknowledge with thanks the enterprise of Pergamon Press in being ready to publish these unusual books. We shall be satisfied if readers find them interesting.

CLOUD NAMES

THE names used for clouds are chosen to describe the processes which cause clouds to look like they do. Full definitions are given in the glossary; this short section explains the basis of the scheme used.

Convection clouds are *cumulus*. Cumulus are composed of newly growing parts sharply outlined, and evaporating parts. They may produce *pileus* while they are growing, and *stratocumulus* when they spread out horizontally. *Cumulonimbus* is a raining cumulus (although it is most often used for clouds with glaciated tops). *Raining* means that there is some form of water *fallout*— rain, hail, snow, drizzle, etc. The spreading out of the tops of cumulus or cumulonimbus produces *anvils.* Downward convection, for example from the base of a layer or anvil, produces *mamma.*

Clouds of falling particles are called *cirrus,* because they look like fibres. The name may also be used for clouds which do not evaporate (and must therefore be composed of ice) and whose particles do not fall appreciably but are drawn out into fibres by the air motion. Rain streaks are usually clearly distinguishable from other forms of cirrus, but not always.

Formless layers are called *stratus.* A layer of fibres is called *cirrostratus,* but a formless layer of frozen particles is simply *ice stratus.*

Castellanus are cumulus which are not connected with convection from below cloud base, but which grow only because of the condensation. The prefix *alto* is used to imply that the cloud is away from direct ground influence, so that castellanus is usually a form of altocumulus.

Wave clouds are clouds formed in waves produced by the flow of air over a hill, a coastline, or some other disturbance of horizontal flow. Wave clouds are neither "alto" nor "cumulus" although they are described in this way in the international classification. Wave clouds may be found scores of miles downwind from the hills that created them; if they move they travel at speeds much less than that of the wind. *Billows,* on the other hand, have a structure which is the result of motions at the layers in which they are formed and they move with the speed of the wind within the layers: they occur in groups of almost equal members, but wave clouds can be solitary. Billows are examples of *cloudlets,* which are small separate clouds which together comprise a large cloud.

A few words are used frequently to add information about the appearance of clouds. Among these are *reticular, iridescent, lenticular, laminated, streets.* But the chief qualifications given in our descriptions concern the physical and dynamical processes by which the clouds have come into being, for example *glaciated, orographic.*

Fog is cloud on the ground; *scud* is cloud formed below the main condensation level.

1. *Cumulus*

2. *Alto-strato-cumulus*

3. *Stratus*

4. *Cirrus*

5. *Waves*

6. *Billows*

MAGNITUDES

(i) *Wind.*

(ii) *Thermal.*

iii) *Large Cumulonimbus.*

iv) *Castellanus.*

THERE are many different kinds of motion which can take place in the atmosphere, and it is easy to find explanations which may seem to be correct until we examine the order of magnitude of the processes invoked. The purpose of this summary is to make clearer what effects can be produced in typical cases.

In the days of Luke Howard electrostatic forces were considered to be of paramount importance, and it was thought possible for particles to be projected through the air upwards from the top of a cloud! We now have a much clearer idea of the magnitudes of the forces and velocities, and our explanations are therefore less liable to serious error. The numbers in heavy type in brackets refer to pictures illustrating the phenomena.

Units 1 m sec^{-1} = 3·6 km hr^{-1} = 2 kt = 2·2 mph = 3·3 fps
1 μ = 1 micron = 10^{-6} m; 100 μ = 0·1 mm.

Horizontal Wind Speeds

Near the surface: Calm—15 m sec^{-1}, exceptionally up to 50 m sec^{-1} in specially exposed places in deep depressions and hurricanes (or typhoons), occasionally up to 100 m sec^{-1}, for example in tornadoes, for a few seconds.

At a height of 1,000 m: Up to 25 m sec^{-1}, occasionally up to 40 m sec^{-1} or more.

At a height of 10,000 m: Up to 50 m sec^{-1}, in jet streams up to 70 m sec^{-1} and exceptionally up to 100 m sec^{-1}.

Vertical Velocity of the Air

Thermal upcurrents (The width of a thermal upcurrent originating at the ground is of the order of $\frac{1}{2}$ to $\frac{1}{3}$ of the height above the ground.)

(i) Below cloud base in sunny weather over land (1) 1-5 m sec^{-1}.

(ii) Inside fair weather cumulus (1) up to 3 m sec^{-1}

(iii) In the updraught into cumulonimbus (19, 28) 5-20 m sec^{-1} according to the stage of development of the storm.

(iv) Inside large cumulonimbus (21) usually up to 15-20 m sec^{-1} and occasionally as large as 30-35 m sec^{-1} in the upper part of the troposphere particularly in isolated violent thunderstorms.

(v) Below cloud base over the open sea (8, 12) usually less than 1-2 m sec^{-1}, but more if there are showers (18).

(vi) Inside clouds over the sea (12), very much as over land but less violent in large cumulonimbus than over land.

(vii) Inside castellanus (33, 35) up to 15 m sec^{-1}, but mostly 3-5 m sec^{-1}.

(viii) In stratocumulus (46), altocumulus (61), and fog under an inversion (115) up to 1 m sec^{-1}.

(ix) In anabatic winds (**55**) 1-2 m sec^{-1} on smaller slopes, but up to 5 m sec^{-1} on extensive steep mountain sides in strong sunshine.

Downdraughts

(i) The downdraughts surrounding thermals below cloud base are generally up to $\frac{1}{3}$ of the strength of the upcurrent they surround, but decrease to much less beyond $\frac{1}{4}$ of the upcurrent width from the edge of it.

(ii) Downdraughts surrounding cumulus towers are usually stronger than around thermals in clear air because of the evaporation, but only in a thin shell surrounding the cloud. They are comparable with the strength of typical updraughts when the whole tower evaporates (**6**) but only endure for about $\frac{1}{4}$ to $\frac{1}{2}$ of the vertical distance of the original updraught.

(iii) In rain or hail inside cloud, up to 10-15 m sec^{-1}.

(iv) In heavy rain below cloud when the cloud base is high (1500-2000 m.a.s.l. or more) as in storms over warm dry inland districts, up to 25m sec^{-1}; but when the cloud base is lower and the air cooler, 10 m sec^{-1} would be larger than average.

(v) In mamma, up to 1-2 m sec^{-1}; more on cumulo-nimbus anvils (**41**) but less under layer clouds (**53, 54, 58**).

(vi) In falling ice trails 1-2 m sec^{+1} (**80**) or less.

(vii) In the wake of an aircraft, up to 20 m sec^{-1} to begin with but decreasing to almost zero 30 sec or so after the aircraft has passed. (**113**)

Subsidence

(i) In steady anticyclones (**8**) around 1 m per min.

(ii) Ahead of moving anticyclones, in cold air ahead of warm fronts (**86, 99**) and behind cold fronts (**103, 104**), up to 1 m sec^{-1}.

(iii) In between thermals (**47**) (not close to them) up to 5 m per min, but up to 1 m sec^{-1} around large cumulus spreading out at the tropopause (**21**).

Ascending motion

(i) In the warm air rising ahead of depressions (**82, 99, 100**), up to 1 m sec^{-1} but more usually around 5 m per min.

(ii) In anabatic winds (see Thermal upcurrents (ix))

Air motion in Waves: (**64, 68, 70**). The up and down component of the velocity of the air is usually up to about $\frac{1}{4}$ of the wind speed at the level in question, according to the inclination of the streamlines. But it can reach as much as half the wind speed in very steep waves, particularly rotors (**71**).

Fall speeds of particles

Water droplets

Radius	1μ	10μ	30μ	100μ	300μ	1mm	3mm	5mm
Fall speed cm sec^{-1}	10^{-1}	1	10	100	300	800	800	800

(iva) *Rain Shower.*

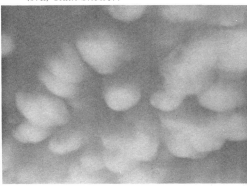
(v) *Mamma.*

(vi) *Behind a Cold Front.*

(vii) *Ahead of a Warm Front.*

(viii) *Steep Wave.*

(ix) *Hailstones.*

(x) *Contrail behind Cold Front absent in dry air.*

Snow flakes — Large 1-2 m sec^{-1}, small $\frac{1}{2}$ m sec^{-1}.

Single ice crystals — Up to 1 m sec^{+1} according to size and shape, but half the speed, or less, of the water droplet of the same volume.

Hail

Radius	5mm	1cm	3cm	5cm
Fall speed, m sec^{-1}	12	20	30	45

Height of Tropopause
  (i) Arctic and Antarctic, down to 5-6 km.
  (ii) Temperature latitudes, around 10 km.
  (iii) Tropics 14-18 km.

Height of Cumulus Cloud base
  (i) Over open oceans, 500-700 m, with no very great variations.
  (ii) Over land, 300-500 m in maritime regions in morning or after rain; but well inland rising to 1000 m or so in winter, and up to 2000 m in summer. In arid regions up to 3000 or 4000 metres.

Difference in height between Condensation level and Ice evaporation level.

Temperature at condensation level, °C.	0	−9	−19	−32	−41
Difference in height, m	0	100	200	300	350
Typical height above sea level in temperate latitudes at equinox, km	2	4	6	7·7	9·2

PLATE SECTION

CUMULUS, PILEUS, ANVIL, STRATOCUMULUS

1. Fair weather cumulus in midmorning in central England. The air below cloud base is well stirred, giving a uniform height to the cloud bases. Each cloud is produced by thermals rising from the sun-warmed ground and has a lifetime of between 5 and 40 minutes according to whether fresh thermals are fed into the base or not.

   The freshly rising towers have a sharp outline. The appearance is darker and ragged where evaporation is taking place (see 2). So long as the evaporation keeps pace with the supply of new thermals, no larger clouds will appear. (See figs 1, 2)

2. Cumulus forming in air as it moves inland from the cooler sea. In the centre is a bright tower, still rising, in which probably all the condensation neuclei are forming cloud droplets. But as soon as the upcurrent stops the smaller droplets quickly evaporate and the visibility in the cloud increases. Less sunlight is scattered back and more is transmitted so that the evaporating cloud looks darker.

   The small clouds at a higher level are produced by the ascent of the air in passing over the hill. (See 64 et seq.)

3. A closer view of a cumulus tower which has pileus on it. This is produced when the air above the rising tower is lifted above its condensation level. Pileus clouds are smooth either because the air in which they are formed is stably stratified or because during their brief existence there is no time for the buoyancy to produce any noticeable upcurrents. (See fig 4)

4. The same as 3 but half a minute later. The tower has risen through the pileus and mixed with the air which formed it.

   The evaporation of the nearer fragment (seen above the rising tower in the picture) has also proceeded noticeably.

5. The cumulus tower seen here is rising through wind shear — the upper air is moving to the right faster than the lower layers — and so it leans to the right. At the same time it is beginning to evaporate and lose the sharp outline (displayed well in the rising tower in 2).

   Above in the distance is cirrus, which remains almost unchanged in appearance for long periods, showing that the ice crystals, of which it is composed, do not evaporate readily like the water droplets of cumulus. (See fig 3).

6. The same as 5 one minute later. The evaporation of the tower is now well under way, and the cloud is sinking as the cooling due to the evaporation produces a negative buoyancy. The evaporation is caused by the mixing of the rising air with the drier environment, and so these clouds cause the whole air mass to become more humid.

7. If the convection reaches up to a stable layer which it has not enough buoyancy to penetrate, the rising air spreads out horizontally; because the buoyancy has disappeared the mixing with the surroundings, and the consequent evaporation, is greatly reduced. An anvil is then produced: in this case it is a water anvil, the cloud being unfrozen. (See fig 5).

   The underside of the overhanging anvil cloud is not the condensation level of the air but is the dividing surface between the cloudy air and the denser clear air below (see 53 and 58).

8. If the spreading out of the thermals occurs at a stable layer just above cloud base the clouds will be very flat. These clouds are typical of the cumulus formed below the inversion of an anticyclone over a warm ocean. The lower layers (up to cloud top) are warmed by convection from the sea, the air above is warmed by subsidence.

1

2

3

4

5

6

7

8

3

9. This view from 5000 metres over the Belgian coast shows how the cumulus forms rapidly over the land in the morning but not over the sea. (The few distant clouds over the sea were present before the cumulus.)

It-is noteworthy that the rate of evaporation from a land surface, particularly with lush vegetation, is much greater than from a sea surface, when the sun is shining.

10. At sunrise the air is stably stratified and the first cumulus appear over the mountain tops, because there the heat of the sunshine is communicated to the air at a higher level. There tends to be anabatic (upslope) flow feeding the cumulus over the mountains and often no cumulus appear over the valleys all day, for there is a slow sinking motion there (55).

11. When the convection is restricted to a layer of fairly uniform depth over a large area and there is a shear of the wind to produce a preferred direction, the cumulus may become aligned in streets along the direction of the shear and at a spacing determined by the depth of the layer. Streets are often short-lived, and disappear when the convection begins to penetrate the stable layer that had temporarily halted its upward growth. Streets are sometimes observed by glider pilots in the pattern of convection even when there are no clouds.

In the distance are some large cumulus, and it is probable that their up motion produced subsidence nearer the observer, and was thus responsible for the stable layer which produced the streets. This view is from 6,000 metres over Northern France.

12. In late autumn particularly the sea is relatively warm, and often supports convection such as is seen here. The clouds are often more closely packed than over land because the shadows do not interfere with the heat supply.

The small patches of stratocumulus are the residue of the water anvils of some of the larger cumulus which have reached up to that level. These may have been formed over the nearby land in the afternoon where the cumulus could have been larger. This view is from 5,500 metres over the Irish Sea.

13. When the shadow of an aircraft on a cloud of water droplets is seen by people in it, it is usually surrounded by a bright, sometimes coloured, glow, called a glory. This is produced by the back scattering of light from the spherical water droplets of which the cloud is composed (the phenomenon is not seen on clouds composed of ice crystals).

Well outside the glory a cloud bow may also be seen (see 27), but this is due to refraction and reflection in the larger droplets.

14. If the size of the cloud droplets near the exterior of the cloud is nearly uniform, several brightly coloured rings may be seen, as here. The same phenomenon is also seen from a mountain top when the observer's shadow falls on a cloud, and it is also called the Spectre of the Brocken because it has become associated particularly with that peak in the Hartz mountains. It has been suggested that this physical phenomenon was seen by the disciples at the transfiguration of Christ, their own shadows being seen beside him at the centre of the glory.

When there are drops of many sizes present, each size produces coloured rings at different angular distances and the colours are therefore smudged, as in 13. Rings as clear as in this picture are therefore not seen when there are strong upcurrents in the cloud, rising to the tops (see text of 2).

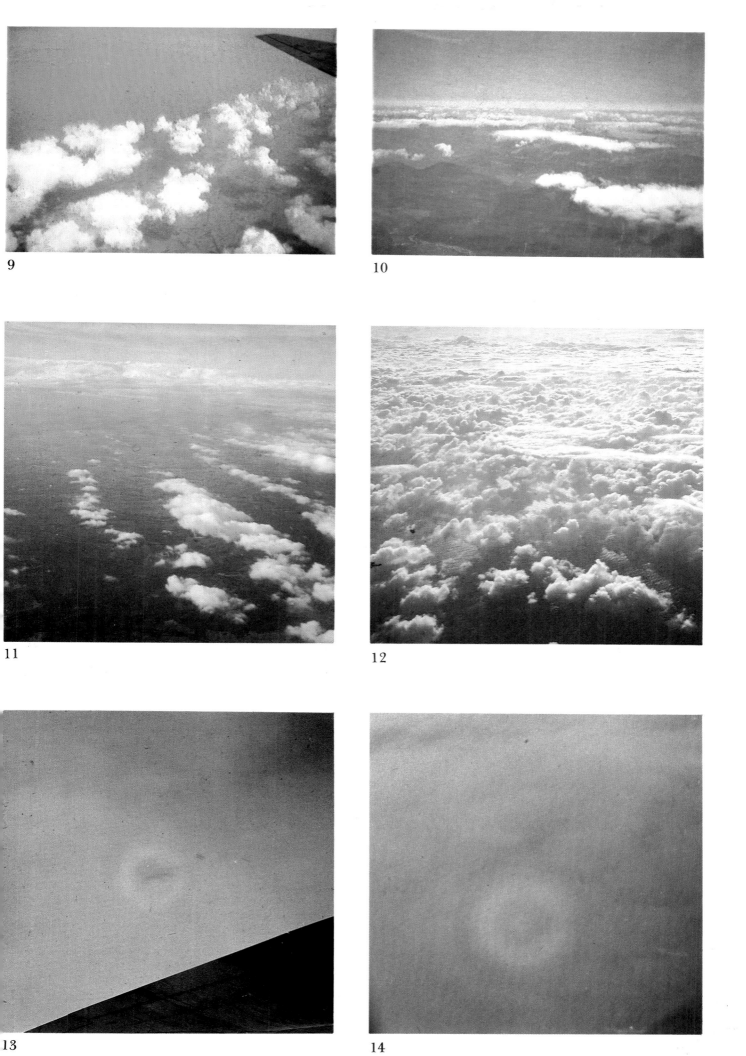

9

10

11

12

13

14

15. In order for the droplets to grow to drizzle or rain size and fall out they must remain in the cloud for sufficient time. There must also be an adequate supply of water vapour. The most favourable conditions when the clouds are small are therefore in summer or in the tropics where temperatures and water vapour content are high, and over the sea where the upcurrents are weaker than over land. In strong upcurrents particles are carried through the cloud to the evaporating region too quickly.

   Here we see warm rain (from unfrozen clouds) from cumulus formed over the sea near Edinburgh in August. Rain is less easily seen than falling ice crystals or snow, but often rainbows can be seen and the particles thereby identified as liquid droplets.

16. When a cloud is glaciated the ice crystals grow and fall out, but their plane surfaces produce a much brighter reflection than water droplets, and the cloud does not have the appearance of evaporation as does the water cloud in 15.

   On reaching a lower and (in this case) drier level the ice crystals begin to evaporate, become smaller, fall slower, and therefore accumulate in a layer. The base of this layer possesses mamma which are downward (negative) thermals of cold air which has been chilled by the evaporation of the ice crystals (see also 80).

   The lower dark clouds on which the sun has already set are wave clouds (see 64 and 65). This picture was taken in Wimbledon.

17. In this close-up of the top of a large cumulus over the Atlantic, the glaciation of the small isolated tower on the left is clear: there is a trail of ice particles falling from it. The large tower on the right has a pileus cloud (see 3) on it.

   There is some wind shear to the left so that the ice trails are inclined down towards the right. This is seen more clearly in 18.

18. The same cloud as 17 a minute later. The small tower is leaning over more and the large tower has penetrated the pileus. Rain is falling and glaciation is evident in the top of the cloud on the right.

   This glaciation is encouraged by the presence of large droplets which freeze more readily than small ones when supercooled.

   The weight of the water accumulated as rain causes a downdraught within the cloud: this is intensified below the cloud by the cooling which results from the evaporation of some of the rain.

19. When the downdraught in the rain reaches the ground it spreads out horizontally. If there is wind shear it will spread out predominantly in the direction in which the upper level wind is stronger. In this case, taken in Bermuda, the shear is to the right.

   Thus a wedge of cold air spreads forward ahead of the rain, scooping up the warm damp air at the ground (or sea) into the cloud where the heat liberated by the condensation generates fresh strong upcurrents (see fig 6).

20. Ice particles reflect the sunlight more effectively than rain and therefore cast a darker shadow and appear darker when seen in front of the sun. These snow streaks appear as a downward extension of the cloud base.

   On reaching the layers which are warmer than 0°C the ice melts and is then scarcely visible. Its fall speed as spherical droplets is greater so that the water is spread into a greater volume.

   In the centre the melting level is clearly seen: on the right the snow casts a shadow on the rain.

21. On reaching the tropopause even the most vigorously rising cumulus will begin to spread out horizontally, and because of the low temperature the anvil thus formed (see 7) will be glaciated. Here, over Bermuda, we see a new tower with pileus, temporarily reaching up above the tropopause level because of the excess buoyancy and upward velocity with which it arrived there.

   This new growth is seen to be close to the older towers which have well spread ice anvils.

   There are evaporating fragments of low level water cloud on the right.

22. This cloud, over Croydon, possesses the classical anvil shape on the left. The new growth is whiter and has sharply outlined towers on the right. There are a few dark fragments (residual water cloud at lower stable layers long since penetrated) in front of these towers.

   From this and other cumulonimbus clouds there is cirrus spread over a large area. Haloes (see 89) can often be seen in this.

   The ice falling from the overhanging anvil serves to cool the air below it and contributes notably to the downdraught which spreads out on the ground (see 19, 28).

15

16

17

18

19

20

21

22

23. This view, over South Wales from about 4,000 metres, shows the larger cumulus penetrating a stable layer below which an almost complete layer of cloud has been formed by the spreading out of cumulus. The nearest cumulus is becoming glaciated so that the parts which have ceased to rise are not evaporating but becoming fibrous.

24. A rising, isolated tower which has become glaciated, seen from 5,500 metres. In the lower part the small water droplets have evaporated leaving only a trail of ice crystals (similar to the small tower in 17), but the top is still rising and sharply outlined. This is an isolated thermal.

Although the sun is immediately behind the cloud, no crepuscular rays (see 45, 92, 111) are seen because the air is clean.

25. Warm rain is seen falling from this cloud (over Wimbledon) and the outside of the part from which droplets are falling has a ragged appearance, not unlike glaciation. The right hand part is producing no rain, and this was proved by observing that no rainbow was seen when it moved into the appropriate position (the wind being from the right). The primary and secondary (faint) rainbows can be seen.

This is an evening cloud, and the upcurrents were too strong earlier in the day for rain to be formed (see 15).

26. A thin ice anvil over N.W. London formed by a rapidly rising isolated tower. The sun has already set on the small fragments of water cloud.

The stem below the spread anvil has falling particles, tending to form mamma, on its exterior, but the anvil itself is composed of much tinier ice crystals which spread in a thin wedge and which have not yet shown effects due to their fall speed.

27. The light from a rainbow is highly polarised because it has undergone a reflection. Cloud bows, which are best seen from fairly close to the cloud, in the evaporating parts of large cumulus where there is a predominance of larger droplets, or in drizzly stratus on hill tops (120), and with the aid of a polarising screen. The polarisation varies in direction with the tangent to the arc so that only part can be well seen at one moment. The polar screen is responsible for the distorted colour in this picture.

Several concentric bows (primary bow and supernumeries) can be seen if the drop size is nearly uniform, the angular spacing depending on the drop size. If there are drops of many sizes present only the primary bows of all the sizes are in phase and so only the primary bow is seen.

28. The rain front advancing across the countryside seen from an aircraft at about cloud base height near Dublin.

Bumpiness in flight is noticeable particularly just above the advancing front of cold air which is some distance, perhaps a mile or so (more if it is advancing downhill) ahead of the rain front. A sudden downward acceleration is clearly experienced on flying into the downdraught air on entering the rain near to cloud base level (see fig. 6).

The arrival of the cold air at the ground causes leaves to rustle, doors and windows to bang, a drop in temperature, and a rise in humidity. The barometer may also show a small jump upwards. (See also 19.)

23

24

25

26

27

28

29. This line of thunderstorms has just passed over from the right and is moving away across southern England. This case is unusual in that instead of the warm moist air being replaced by cool air, the warm air was advancing and moving up over the top of the cold air. The cold downdraught air is moving away more slowly than the warm surface air is advancing, and the uppermost cloud is also moving away more slowly, and so, relative to the line of newly developing cumulus, is spreading out towards the warm air. This may be regarded in some respects as a line of warm front thunderstorms.

30. Usually, after the passage of a line of showers (or thunderstorms) the warm sultry air at the ground is replaced by a layer of cooler, rather calm, air spread out on the ground by the downdraught. Being coldest at the bottom this air is very stable at first (i.e. until the sun has shone for some time on the ground beneath it), and smoke (in this case from Southampton) accumulates in horizontal layers, making the stability clearly visible.

In the distance is more vigorous cumulus over the sea. This picture was taken in the early morning, and the English Channel was warm enough to produce showers during the night which moved inland with the wind (see also 41, 81).

31. After a shower the ground is wet, and often still warm beneath the surface, and frequently steams in the sunshine. The lowest layers of air thus become much damper than the layers above, and so have a lower condensation level (unlike the air in 1). Convection thus produces fragmentary cumulus, often called scud, at various levels below the main cloud base. In this picture (Wimbledon) the sun is just breaking through after the passage of a line of showers at a cold front.

32. Because of the uniformity of the sea surface, cold fronts and lines of showers are much better defined than over land. Squall lines at which there is first a gusting of the wind, then the passage of rain followed by a rapid clearance and a change of wind direction as the cold air arrives, are often quite pronounced. In the air wetted by rain there are fragments of scud below the main base. The light beyond is often clear and bright well before the rain stops. This squall line is moving away after passing over the ship.

33. Cumulus over land (such as 1, 2, 9) acquire most of their buoyancy from the warm ground. Over the sea no thermals with a temperature more than a fraction of a degree warmer than the surroundings can be formed, but often the air is very unstable above the condensation level once the heat of condensation is released. Cumulus towers then rise at great speed and assume a much taller appearance, called castellanus, than when the surroundings are only marginally unstable for cloudy air.

These are seen near Bermuda. Their shape may be contrasted with flat cumulus (8) in stable air.

34. Castellanus like 33 are formed at a higher level when the condensation is produced by some other mechanism than heating from below. Here a layer is seen sprouting when it has been formed in air that is very unstable for cloud.

This type is often called floccus, and this example is over Wimbledon; it is typical of very unstable but rather dry air.

35. This castellanus (over Wimbledon) is more common than the floccus of 34. The cumulus sprouts from lines formed probably in very nearly saturated air lifted slightly over small hills, and it shows the usual sharp outline on the rising towers. The environment through which they are rising is less dry than in 34.

36. This line of cloud was formed over the 500 ft. high Epsom Downs south of London. It is a wave cloud but the air is unstable for cloud and so castellanus towers are sprouting from the top.

29

30

31

32

33

34

35

36

SHOWERS, CUMULUS, MAMMA

37 and 38. Two wide angle pictures are used to compose this 180° panorama of the sky on a showery day. On the left in the distance is a glaciated anvil, and some small evaporating cumulus appear above it in the picture. There is less growth in the centre because the view is towards an estuary up which the wind is blowing. On the right can be seen layers formed by the spreading out of cumulus, and this moistens the stable layer so that small wave clouds, such as that seen in the middle of the picture at the top, are formed by flow over even very small hills or as pileus over newly growing cumulus.

39. Cumulus forming streets in mid-morning. These are formed (see 11) when the convection is limited to a layer of fairly uniform depth over a wide area, and this situation may prevail for only a short time in the morning. Some streets are formed extending downwind from good thermal sources. There tends to be a fairly uniform updraft under the streets (sometimes biassed towards one side) with a somewhat weaker, wider downdraught in between. The tops usually behave like individual cumulus towers.

40. Cumulus forming in a light onshore wind over a range of coastal mountains in Wales. The estuary and sea are clear of cloud, but over the land convection is vigorous, and pileus surmounts many of the rising towers. The stable layer in which the pileus is formed has also accumulated some layer cloud.

41. The rear edge of a receding line of showers showing how the rapidly ascending towers spread out at the tropopause and have mamma, produced by the falling snow, on their overhanging anvils.

Down the underside of this overhanging cloud the cold air, which will spread out on the ground, descends and replaces the warm air. **30** was taken soon after this picture.

42. This single street of cumulus was formed along the coast of Caernarvonshire in the evening when the wind was blowing nearly parallel to the coast from right to left. There was no cloud between it and the coast because of insufficient heating, while beyond it cloud was inhibited by the shadow of the line itself, the sun being fairly low. Beyond the shadow larger cumulus is forming over the higher ground.

43. These showers had kept themselves going until evening. Several of the tops are well glaciated and fibrous, some are quite fresh. There is also a considerable accumulation of cloud at the stable layer two thirds of the way up.

Nearer to the observer is a solitary fragment of ice cloud, the sole remnant of an otherwise evaporated cloud. These ice particles are falling and mamma are formed at the right hand end where they are evaporating.

44. A few solitary cumulus are penetrating through the stable layer which has trapped large amounts of pollution and made the upper limit of most of the convection clearly visible in the low late afternoon sun. There are also patches of cloud, presumably formed by the spreading out of earlier cumulus, now otherwise evaporated, at the stable layer. The shadow of the cloud on the haze is clearly seen on the left (top) (see also **109, 110**).

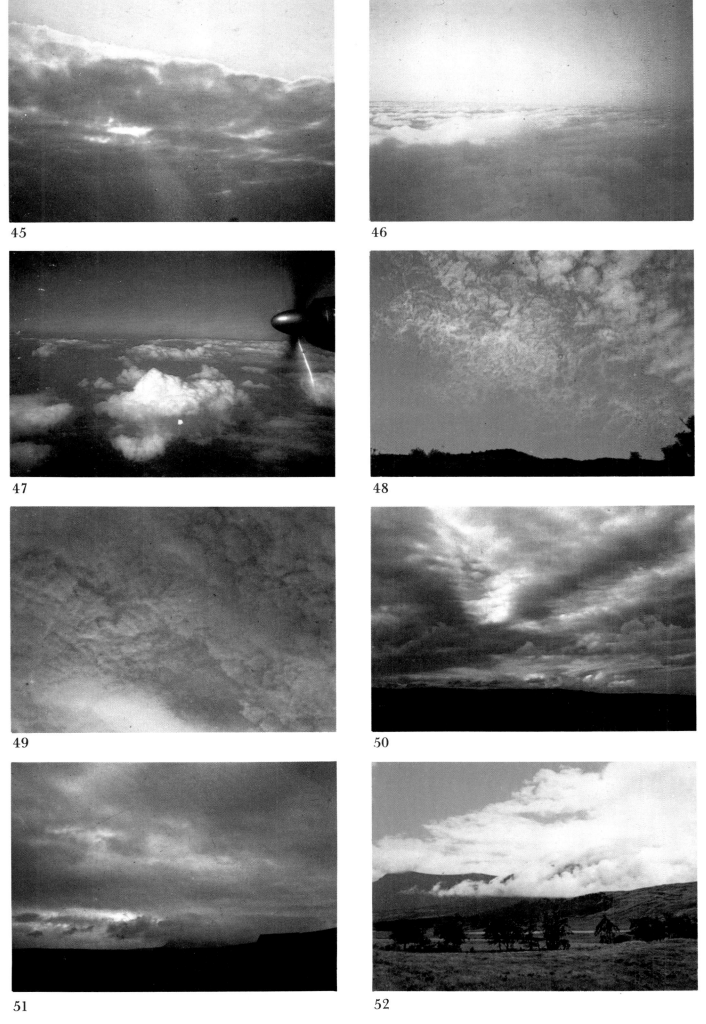

45

46

47

48

49

50

51

52

15

53. The mamma seen on the underside of this layer are characteristic of a layer formed by the spreading out of cumulus (7) which is then subjected to up and down motion over hills. In the down motion the cloud is warmed more slowly than the air below it and, on becoming cooler than it, sinks into it, forming the mamma.

54. Mamma are best seen at sunset when they are obliquely illuminated by direct sunlight. They are often difficult to see when the sun is higher because they are rather tenuous, most of the smaller drops, which give a cloud its sharp outline, having been evaporated by the descending motion.

55. When a slope, particularly one facing the sun, is heated, the convection warms the layer closest to the hillside, and this produces an anabatic (upslope) flow, with rather fragmentary cumulus formed in it. No cumulus are formed in the air at the same height away from the hillside because it remains stably stratified (see fig. 7).

   The cumulus form preferentially over the hill crests (see 10).

56. This is a distant view of the Lleyn Peninsula (N. Wales). The sun on the south facing slopes produced cumulus. Later in the evening it produced an anabatic flow on the N.W.-facing slopes, and the air to the north had a lower condensation level. Consequently cumulus was formed at a lower level.

   There was no cumulus over the sea. The cirrus is typical fair-weather cloud, probably the residue of a frontal cloud carried by the strong wind at that level far from the scene of main activity.

57. This isolated mountain peak (near Chambéry) is acting as a preferential source of thermals. This is the typical appearance of cloud formed in this way in the morning, carried away from the source by the wind at higher levels.

58. The mamma on the base of this water anvil are well developed at the time the spreading is taking place. The source cloud is off to the right. There was very little wind on this occasion.

59. There was flow up both sides of this mountain ridge (Snowdon), but the wind was predominantly from the right, while the air on the left was damper. The flow separated from the salient edge in the manner shown in fig. 12(ii).

60. The base of this cloud is illuminated by sunshine reflected from the sea surface. By contrast with the sharply defined base of the clouds in 53 and 58 where moist air is flowing over drier air with a discontinuity of humidity at the cloud base, the base of this cumulus is seen to be more diffuse. Air is passing through this cloud base, and cloud condenses in it as it rises, and evaporates as it sinks.

53

54

55

56

57

58

59

60

17

61. This cloud is called *alto*cumulus because there are no currents from the ground reaching it. It is losing heat by radiation into space from the tops and gaining by radiation from the ground below. It is also gaining a much smaller amount by the absorption of sunshine. Because of this loss at the top and gain of heat at the bottom it becomes unstable, and the convection is arranged in billows across the wind shear; but the motion within the cloudlets is very slow. The cloudlets move with the wind (see fig. 9).

62. This is another example of billows, in which the static instability appears less important because the billows are not cumulus as in **61**. They appear arched on top as if they were in the upper half of the roll motion (see fig. 9). They are at a level where most of the cloud is composed of ice crystals, but the newly formed billows stand out brightly against the tenuous ice cloud and are initially composed of supercooled water (iridescence can often be seen in them (see **105**)), but in a few minutes they become infected with ice and are glaciated like the row near the top of the picture. The sun is behind the house.

63. These billows do not appear to correspond to a cellular or roll-like motion. They appear in less than a minute in a layer of cloud, but are not waves because they move with the wind. They last for five to ten minutes, sometimes longer. The wave-like clouds in the lower half of the picture lie along the wind, and are not ordinary waves. The billows appear to lie across the direction of shearing motion, but the motion responsible for neither of these cloud forms has been properly elucidated.

64. The lenticular clouds are in the crests of the wave motion in the air streaming across the hills of north England. They are more or less stationary relative to the ground and are mountain wave clouds. They lie at the top of a moist layer at which there is an inversion, and at which the wave amplitude is greater than above and below (see figs. 8, 10).

    The billows seen in one of the wave clouds move with the wind through the wave, fresh ones forming on the near (upwind) side, those on the downwind side evaporating.

    There is a patch of early morning stratus on the hill top on the left.

65. In the early morning, before the convection from the ground reaches up to cloud level the wave clouds over hills may be very smooth, particularly if there is a stable layer, with drier air above, at their top. But convection makes them become like cumulus, and already in this case in Scotland, the lower level wave cloud has undergone this change. They are often described as stratocumulus. Although the individual pieces of cumulus move with the wind the position of the patch remains the same relative to the hill.

    The finger-like streamers from the left edge of the small wave on the right are corrugations along the direction of the wind (see **69**). They occur when there is strong wind shear but no static instability, and the instability is due to the curvature of the flow in the waves.

66. This is a typical complicated wave cloud sky of north England (or any hilly area), with the waves revealed by the clouds at different levels. The clouds tend to lie across the wind, but at the highest level can be seen two lines of orographic cirrus (see **77**). The strip on the right is still showing a billowed structure (see **90**), which disappeared after about two minutes as the cloud became glaciated. This type is often called cirro-cumulus.

67. This low level wave cloud, viewed almost vertically upwards towards the sun, illustrates how, where the air enters the wave at the left edge the distribution of humidity is fairly uniform; but the instability due to the condensation produces cumulus cloudlets, so that on the evaporating edge of the wave the cloud is lumpy. The cloudlets can be seen moving through the wave, which remains stationary. There is no evidence of shear in this cloud (see fig. 8).

68. There are two layers of wave clouds seen here. The upper layer has been turned into altocumulus cloudlets which move through the stationary waves with the wind. Those which evaporate on leaving one wave reappear in the next.

    At the lower level the air is stable and the wave pattern is complicated and unsteady, because the lowest layers of air become more stable when the sun goes down.

    These waves are formed over the small hills of north London.

61

62

63

64

65

66

67

68

WAVE CLOUDS

69. Normally the lowest layers of air are stirred by convection (by day) so that there is no discontinuity of humidity at the cloud base, which is therefore horizontal and at the condensation level. In this case a layer at about 1,700 metres is lying above drier air so that the base is distorted into the shape of the waves to produce the effect of a vaulted roof over London.

There are also corrugations along the direction of the wind and across the waves, and these are often seen on the smooth tops of wave clouds, though rather rarely on the base (see 65).

71. This shows the "Sierra Wave" in the Owens Valley in California (see frontispiece and 79). The air descends the steep mountain slope on the right (seen in 79) and the cloud capping the mountains evaporates. It then rises from the valley floor into the first lee wave, producing a line of cloud parallel to the mountains (see also 75). In this line the lowest cloud is cumulus, showing that the condensation produces instability but the higher cloud is smooth wave cloud. The line of cumulus is in the rotor (see fig. 11) and cloud with this appearance is often called a rotor cloud.

The topmost wave cloud has short ice trails emerging from it but these are evaporated in the strong downdraught.

73. This "Pile d'Assiettes" seen near Marseilles is a rather spectacular example of a laminated wave cloud. These can be seen in any hilly region (see 98) if the airstream consists of several humid layers with less humid layers interposed. The pile of plates lies in the crest of a wave, and such clouds are common over the isolated islands of the southern oceans.

The mechanism whereby the atmosphere contrives to produce these thin humid layers is uncertain, but they are probably formed by the shearing over of the humid towers due to cumulonimbus, in between which the air is much drier.

75. Trough and wave in the lee of Corsica. The northern tip of the island lies under the bank of cloud on the right. This cloud evaporates as the air descends the eastern slopes in a wind from the west. Through the gap in the wave trough can be seen a lower layer of cloud also evaporating at the coast. The gap in the lee of the coast is followed by a lee wave, whose cloud can be seen in the bottom left of the picture. Above this is a higher wave cloud, whose base is illuminated by the setting sun. There is no cloud at this level over the mountain, which shows that at that level the lee wave is larger than the mountain wave. A cold front had recently passed through and large cumulus are seen, with the remains of a distant glaciated anvil on the right. There is more cloud also over the main mass of the island, but the air between the cumulus is stable enough for lee waves.

70. In the trough between two wave crests a hole in a layer of cloud often appears. In this case it appears over an estuary in north Wales. The arched top of the wave cloud over the hill can be seen through the hole. The cloud positions are stationary, but the wind is nearly gale force from left to right.

72. This is a typical wave sky (north Wales) ahead of an approaching depression, when the cloud layers thicken up, but remain stable, and the upper wind increases.

These smooth topped wave clouds (see fig. 10) tend to lie in lines more or less parallel to the mountain ridges and are best developed by those ridges which lie across the wind, so that they tend also to lie across the wind.

74. Wave clouds seen in the early morning when the air is stable, in a situation (approach of a front) when the upper wind is becoming strong. It is also becoming moister and contrails (113) easily form at high levels: in this case a trail casts its dark shadow on the cloud below.

76. This is a "mother of pearl" cloud (so called because of the iridescence often seen in them but not visible in this case perhaps because of too long an exposure which turns colours to white on film), over Norway, seen some time after the sun has set on the clouds below. They are at a height of about 28 kilometres.

They have the same appearance as ordinary water wave clouds (whose iridescence is less easily seen because of the brightness of the surrounding sky) and in this case a trail of ice cloud (composed of those droplets that have frozen) emerges from the lee side.

The temperature of these clouds is much lower than in ordinary wave clouds and orographic cirrus (77), but/and the freezing of all the water droplets is probably prevented by their small size (0.15μ, which is about a fortieth of ordinary cloud droplets).

69

70

71

72

73

74

75

76

21

77. Wave clouds seen near Loch Ness (Scotland). The wind is from the right and the topmost wave cloud has a trail of orographic cirrus emerging from it, because the droplets freeze almost immediately. They do not evaporate on the lee side of the wave because the air does not descend below the ice evaporation level (see fig. 8). Low level wave clouds can be seen also.

In summer wave clouds are usually seen much better developed in the early morning or evening. The convection instability during the day inhibits well developed waves by causing separation and anabatic flow which stops the air flow from following the ground profile (see 111).

78. Orographic cirrus is also fairly common over small hills, in this case south of London. The wind is blowing along these lines of cirrus from the distance on the left towards the top right of the picture, and the cloud occupying the upper left corner of the picture is recognisable as a wave because of the thickening of the cloud there. The cloud does not evaporate as it emerges from the wave because it is glaciated.

79. Bands of cirrus of an approaching warm front lying along the wind (the jet stream) above the Sierra Nevada of California (see frontispiece and 71). The ends of the bands can be seen at the leading edge of the cloud, and the band structure is probably due to the cloud having appeared first as orographic cirrus over the mountains. (See also 76–78 and 90.)

80. Trails of ice crystals falling from castellanus which has completely glaciated. Some cumulus castellanus in the distance have not yet turned completely to fallout. The fastest falling particles in the centre of each cloud give the trail a conical appearance, and there is probably a stronger downdraught in the centre. This fibrous appearance can only be seen in ice clouds. When the trails reach a layer where there is wind shear and some evaporation, mamma are formed on them (see also 16 and 43). The blue sky has been darkened by the use of a polarising screen.

81. This cirrus represents its type better than 80. It is thought to be formed by ice particles falling from a source cloud, as in 80, and carried away to one side by shear. Undoubtedly the trails lie along the direction of shear, and the particles are falling, but often it appears that the particles are not all generated at the top of the trail. These clouds are difficult to study because they undergo only small changes as they move across the sky.

They are commonly said to be associated with approaching warm fronts; but this example was seen on a day of heavy showers over southern England (shown in 41), and they can be seen in many types of weather. They contrast markedly with the woolly appearance of the cumulus.

82. The typical criss-cross appearance of the cirrus of an approaching warm front. The lines from low right to top left are along the wind from the north west (the jet stream), and are often lines of orographic cirrus (see 79 and 90). The trails of falling particles lie across these lines because the warm air is spreading in that direction over the sinking cold air ahead of the front; and they reveal the direction of shear at that level. They show that development is taking place.

The post in the foreground is blurred because the picture was taken from a moving train near Leicester (England).

83. Streaks of cirrus extending across the whole sky. These, again, lie along the direction of wind shear, but not across the direction of the wind. No development is indicated, and they are associated with fine weather. The cloud could be called cirro stratus—a fibrous layer.

Haloes are not common in these very thin layers of cirrus though mock suns are often seen when the sun is low.

84. Lines of cirrus in a jet stream (the wind blowing strongly along the lines), but with no development—the trails of falling crystals are almost vertical. This sky was seen over Wimbledon near the stationary front in the region of subsidence between two depressions.

77

78

79

80

81

82

83

84

85. Cirrus showing streaks of falling particles and an increase in density towards the west, but no very definite arrangement in lines. The streaks are directed towards the denser cloud (as in 82), indicating development. The patches of wave cloud over the small hills to the south-west of London show that the first patches of middle level cloud appear over hills as a depression approaches. The stable air and strong upper winds are favourable for the formation of waves.

86. The cirrus streaks are rather like those of 83 but thicken towards the West. Here (as in 85) the first middle level clouds to appear as a warm front approaches are wave clouds, showing laminations in this case (see 73, 74).

The cumulus which had been larger earlier in the day is much reduced by the subsidence ahead of the approaching front and by the cutting off of the sunshine by the cirrus (see 99).

87. A closer view of falling cirrus trails, taken from an aircraft at 6,000 metres. The appearance is very much like falling snow and the cloud very tenuous.

Cumulus protruding through a layer formed by the spreading of earlier cumulus is seen below, near Dijon, France.

The crystals produce their own downdraughts of the order of 1 or 2 metres per second, as they evaporate into the surrounding air and/or because of their weight; their appearance is thus rather like the underside of a cumulonimbus anvil (see 96). From the ground the cloud looked rather like 85.

88. In patches of cirrus mock suns (parhelia) are often seen. The colours are separated by refraction in hexagonal ice prisms with their axes vertical, and the mock sun is seen at about 23° from the sun and at the same altitude. The specular reflection from the surfaces of the same prisms produces the parhelic circle, a white bright region in the cloud horizontally through the sun. Part of such a circle is seen here to the right of the coloured region but the part of this parhelic circle to the right of the mock sun (i.e. away from the sun) is much brighter because of the light refracted through crystals whose faces are not oriented to refract the rays through the minimum angle. The blue end of the spectrum is thus not seen in the mock sun.

This mock sun (and parhelic circle) was seen in an aircraft condensation trail, though this is not particularly common because the particles in such a trail are usually very numerous and small and have no preferred orientation.

89. The 22 degree halo is formed by the same kind of refraction as the mock sun (88) but in prisms whose axes are perpendicular to the plane through the sun, the observer, and the prism. Thus in the cloud, prisms must be oriented in all directions.

The brightest haloes are usually seen when the sun is high in the sky, because they are then formed by a greater proportion of the prisms when they are nearly horizontal; but they may be seen at any time of day. They are also often very clear round the moon. They are best when the cloud is diffuse and not drawn into streaks by shear: the crystals falling slowly and rather far apart. Haloes are often seen in the cirrus ahead of a warm front but by no means always, nor only at such a time.

This is the most common of all the halo phenomena.

90. This is an isolated streamer of orographic cirrus oriented along the wind direction, with its characteristic transverse striations.

Below in the distance are seen wave clouds over the lower hills. This streamer originated over Snowdonia about eighty miles upwind of, and behind, the observer.

High up, and to the left of the middle of the picture is a roll of wave cloud. This is rather like an ordinary wave cloud but does not last long. It is possibly in a small rotor at about 2 or 3 kilometres above the ground. Such clouds often appear to be stationary at first (as the rotor develops) but then drift away downwind (as the rotor collapses).

99

100

101

102

103

104

105

106

107. The golden light of dawn is often not recognised in its full brilliance by the eye which quickly accustoms itself to it. The cooling by radiation which has caused a copious dew to be deposited on the grass has made the air very stable and the mist has not yet cleared from the distant field where the shadow of the hill delayed the arrival of sunshine. The cottage smoke quickly levels out and is carried with little mixing for some distance.

108. Before the sun appears above the horizon the sky colours are often predominantly the extremes of sky blue and deep red of the cirrus clouds when first illuminated. The stratus patches are not yet directly illuminated.

On the water are long calm streaks where the water is unruffled by the wind. This is probably where upwelling brings to the surface material of organic origin which substantially increases the surface tension of the water.

109. From above an inversion it is easy to see that the pollution produced at the ground is often confined to a shallow layer of air close to the ground by the great stability of the air. Such high stability is characteristic of the winter when the nights are long and convection feeble by day.

Most striking are the sharp horizons visible on these haze tops from above.

110. When looked at towards the sun a haze top can be dazzlingly bright, and the ground below invisible. In this case, in late afternoon, a layer of stratus has been broken up by convection during the day and some of the thermals are just protruding through the inversion at about 2000 metres as small cumulus clouds. The high humidity just below the inversion undoubtedly contributes to the poor visibility (see 112).

111. The air below an inversion is well stirred by convection and the pollution well distributed (see also 45). The cloud seen here is of the same type as 8 but is over the hills of South Wales. The gaps in the clouds do not correspond with the valleys, which lie NW-SE, but move along with the wind, showing that the air was flowing across the valley tops without descending the hillsides. The wind was from the NE and there was an upslope flow up the SW facing slopes with separation (see 59 and fig. 12 (iii)) near the tops of the mountain ridges.

112. Where there are breaking waves small droplets are thrown into the air and evaporate partially, filling the air with a haze of hygroscopic salt particles. The droplets are mostly produced when bubbles of air carried under by the breaking waves burst through the surface, or when the thin water films which form surface froth are fragmented. The lower layers contain many more particles than the air at cliff top level.

Salt particles are enlarged by the absorption of water and thereby reduce the visibility when the relative humidity exceeds 70%, even when no cloud or fog droplets are formed.

113. Condensation trails are left by aircraft when the air is sufficiently cold for the mixture of air and exhaust to be saturated (see 119). This does not usually happen except when the temperature is close to or below −40°C, in which case the cloud freezes almost instantaneously and does not readily evaporate. The cloud is then spread out by any wind shear which may be present. Below is a street of small cumulus.

114. Scud is formed over a surface from which evaporation is taking place so that the air near the surface has a lower condensation level than the air through which it is rising. Scud occurs at a rather variable height below the main cloud base or condensation level. It may also occur in air into which rain has been evaporated and which subsequently becomes lifted again, as in the case illustrated here. It is usually seen to be rising rapidly and often evaporates during ascent because of mixing with drier air. The first convection cloud formed in the morning as the dew dries off the ground in the sunshine is a form of scud (see 31, 52, 55).

107

108

109

110

111

112

113

114

115. During a clear night the air in the valleys may become so cold that they are filled with fog. In calm weather the fog top becomes horizontal and the fog edge lies along a contour of the hillsides. Close to the edge where the fog is thinnest the sunshine is beginning to 'burn it up'—evaporate it by warming the ground.

116. At sunset the ground often cools so rapidly that stratus (or fog) is formed in the thin layer of air chilled by proximity to it. This is particularly true of mountains which are close to the condensation level of the air. In these circumstances the cloud can be seen draining down the slopes, and has the appearance of a cloth draped over them. This mountain, in Wales, is about 350 metres high.

117. Sea fog is prevalent particularly where the coastal water is colder than the open sea. This example, in a southerly airstream over Cape Cod, also shows how the shallow water immediately adjacent to the beach is warmed by sunshine and partially evaporates the fog by convection currents. The fog is evaporated over the warm land by day.

118. When tropical air moves across N.W. Europe sea fog is common. This example shows it being dispersed as it crosses the coast of Wales. The convection currents can set up as fragmentary cumulus but it is very quickly evaporated in the drier air above. The anabatic flow up the hills is deep compared with the katabatic flow illustrated in 116.

119. 'Arctic sea smoke' is the name given to the fog formed when cold air from snow covered land moves over warm sea. Such fog is often seen near the Lofoten Islands of Norway. It is also seen in bathrooms, or over warm rivers early in the morning in the autumn, as here.

   The cloud is formed by the mixing of the warm, almost saturated air at the water surface with much colder air blowing across from the neighbouring fields such as are seen in 107 (taken on the same morning). The mixture is supersaturated at an intermediate temperature. Except for condensation trails (113) this mode of cloud formation is very rare in the atmosphere away from the ground or sea.

120. 'Hill fog' is the name given to stratus cloud in contact with hill tops. On the windward side there is often copious drizzle from these clouds and the rainfall is considerably augmented by the capture of cloud particles on the grass, and on trees with small spiky leaves such as pine, if this type of cloud is common. The base is often very sharply defined on the lee side, as here (N. Wales), where the well stirred cloud evaporates in the descending air.

121. A sea of cloud filling a valley up to the level of an inversion, undisturbed by convection from the ground because the sun is only just rising. A sun pillar is visible in the tenuous cirrus. This is produced by reflection from the faces of ice prisms whose axes are horizontal.

122. In the evening a sun facing slope may have an anabatic wind blowing up it although the air generally has already become stable. The continued evaporation from vegetation whose roots are still warm lowers the condensation level of the shallow layer of air which forms the upslope current so that the condensation level (1,000 metres, here) is lower in this air than in the air generally in which cumulus had formed with base at 1,500 metres during the day. A fallstreak of cirrus is seen beyond.

115

116

117

118

119

120

121

122

DIAGRAM OF CLOUD MECHANISMS

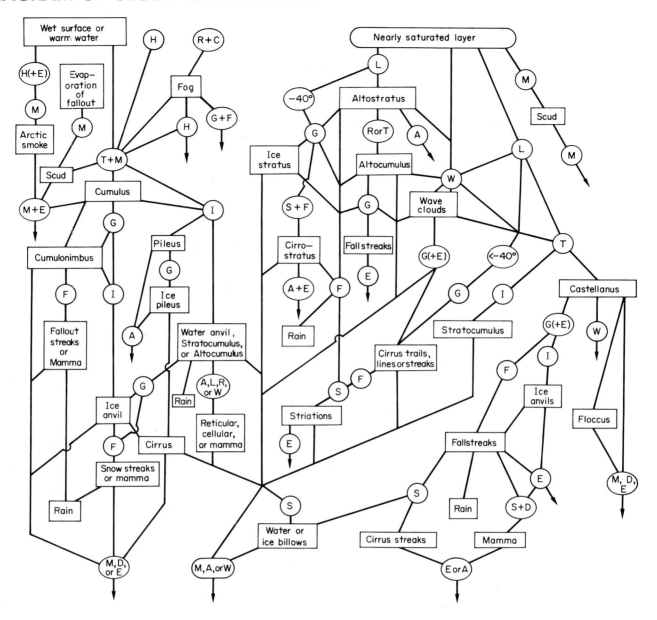

List of Symbols

A   Subsidence—sinking motion of the air (typical of anticyclones).

C   Non-adiabatic cooling (i.e. by processes other than lifting).

D   Downdraughts due to cooling by evaporation.

E   Evaporation of cloud particles into unsaturated air.

F   Fallout of water or ice particles.

G   Glaciation of cloud particles.

H   Non-adiabatic heating e.g. by warm ground.

I   Inversion or stable layer.

L   Widespread ascending motion (lifting).

M   Mixing.

R   Cooling by radiation into space.

S   Shear.

T   Thermal convection (in cloud or in clear air).

W   Waves or other up or down motion due to hills and mountains.

Diagram of Cloud Mechanisms

By following tracks down the diagram the mechanisms producing various kinds of cloud can be considered. The rectangular boxes contain visible phenomena and the round boxes the physical circumstances or mechanisms which must be present to produce the phenomena. The downward pointing arrows indicate the disappearance of the cloud, and "rain" includes all kinds of water fallout (drizzle, snow, sleet, hail, etc.).

The diagram does not contain clouds of smoke, blown sand or snow (sandstorms and blizzards), tornadoes, contrails or other artificial forms of water or ice cloud, nor streets and larger scale formations. The various refraction, diffraction, reflection and colour optical phenomena are not included. The growth of ice particles in supersaturated air inside clouds, a process which causes fallout, is not referred to specifically.

In some boxes there are alternatives, but not necessarily all are appropriate to all the tracks through them. Thus cirrus does not produce water billows, but only ice billows. Many possibilities may have been omitted, some deliberately, others perhaps in error. Thus, for example, it is possible that the stratocumulus which appears in a box by itself might become glaciated, but this is very rare. It is also possible that altocumulus might appear out of clear air, and this is only possible, according to the left hand part of the diagram, via the convection mechanism, and not by widespread or orographic liftings: but if altocumulus appears out of clear air it is almost certain that there has either been the anvil forming process or convection within a layer of altostratus (as envisaged in the diagram) within the same air not long before.

Questions may be asked as starting points for discussion, e.g.:

(1) Why is it possible to pass through the diagram by some tracks through only one rectangular box, while some rectangular boxes cannot be the only one on any track?

(2) Why don't cirrus trails from wave clouds ever have mamma?

(3) Where is the cloud often called cirrocumulus represented?

(4) Could mamma form on fallstreaks from glaciated patches of altocumulus?

(5) Can the diagram be broken up naturally into a few large sections which represent the main basic cloud forms—convection clouds, layer clouds, fibrous clouds, and wave clouds?

(6) Can it readily be augmented so as to include the items listed above as not included in it?

(7) A question of topology—assuming that the diagram is complete and correct, can it be reorganised so as to be made simpler?

Questions such as these may require acute observation of developing clouds, as well as clear thought, if the answers are to be found.

The diagram may be used to suggest lines of enquiry: could any of the boxes, which are not at present linked, be linked? Have any of the cloud forms illustrated in the book been erroneously omitted? Can the arrangement of boxes be improved upon so as to illustrate the physics and dynamics better, quite apart from topological questions? New arrangements might suggest new links and new sequences of events which might explain new clouds which are observed and features formerly unnoticed may become obvious.

TYPES OF MOTION

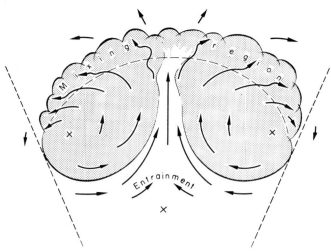

1. *Thermal.* This is a mass of buoyant air rising with axial symmetry through its surroundings. It grows (a) by *mixing* over its upper surface with the air into which it is advancing (b) by the *entrainment* into its base of exterior air which becomes mixed when it rises into the mixing region. The arrows show the relative strengths of the velocities in the circulation, and the thermal as a whole rises at somewhat less than half the strength of the upcurrent in its centre. On account of the mixing and entrainment it increases in size along a cone (indicated by the dotted lines) of semi-vertical angle about 15°. The thermal turns itself inside out, the mixing penetrating to all parts of it, in rising about $1\frac{1}{2}$ diameters.

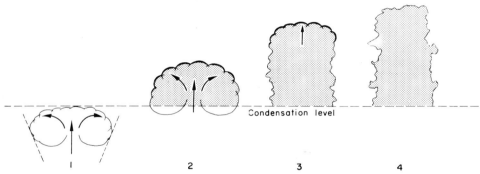

2. *Cumulus Tower.* Above the condensation level the thermal becomes visible as cloud and rises through stably stratified surroundings, which oppose entrainment; also the mixing begins to cause evaporation which reduces the upward motion and may even produce downward motion around the widest part. The thermal soon ceases to grow in size and ultimately the mixing and evaporation affect the whole volume of the thermal and the upward motion ends. The stable stratification causes the diluted parts to be *eroded* and left behind as a visible cloud (2, 33).

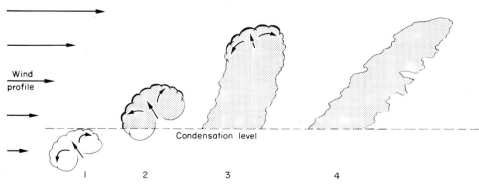

3. *Cumulus Tower in Wind Shear.* When it rises through a shearing wind the thermal has its axis tilted. At stage 2 the rolling over motion in the downwind half of the thermal can sometimes be seen when clear air is entrained (92). Erosion occurs, as in fig. 2, and the tower is seen to lean over before it is completely evaporated (5, 6).

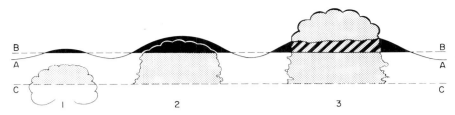

4. *Pileus*. If there is an inversion originally at A and the air just below it has condensation level at B, it may be lifted up by the rise of a thermal below it so that a smooth pileus cloud is formed (3, 4). In the diagram it is supposed that the thermal has condensation level at C, but if it were higher the thermal could well not be visible below the pileus. At stage 2 the thermal appears to have a smooth rather than the usual knobbly top (17). The thermal will sink back if it is not buoyant enough to penetrate the inversion, but otherwise it will penetrate the pileus which will be seen as a smooth collar just before the sinking motion around the thermal causes it to disappear.

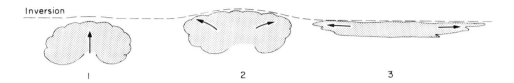

5. *Anvil*. When a thermal, or any other more complex upcurrent, arrives at an inversion which it has not enough buoyancy to penetrate, it spreads out beneath it after temporarily overshooting it. The cloud which spreads out is the anvil cloud. Mixing is reduced so that evaporation is slower on the exterior of an anvil than on the outside of a cumulus (7, 58, 96).

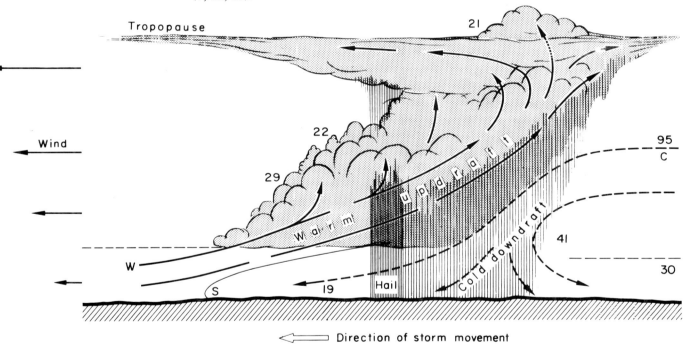

Direction of storm movement

6. *Self-propagating Shower*. When there is sufficient shear this configuration of motion may develop. The rising air, starting at W, is lifted by the cold squall, S (19), the cold air being below the continuous line. It is lifted through an inversion, which has been sufficiently stable to prevent much ordinary thermal convection through it, and then through its condensation level whereafter it can rise to the tropopause, most of it along an inclined path. It spreads out in all directions at the tropopause (21) and the fallout produces mamma on the underside of the anvil (41). Some cumulus towers rise out of the upcurrent (22, 95). Most of the anvil is carried forward with the high level wind, but most of the rain falls into air at level C, which is overtaking the storm. This air is cooled by the fallout and descends to the ground spreading out there predominantly in the forward direction because of its greater speed, and scooping up warm slower-moving air at W which is being overtaken by the storm. The cold air is decelerated and ultimately left spread out on the ground beneath an inversion behind the storm (30). Shear, such as that shown on the left, is necessary, otherwise the fallout from the updraught cannot produce a downdraught in air above the base of the cloud and outside the cloud.

37

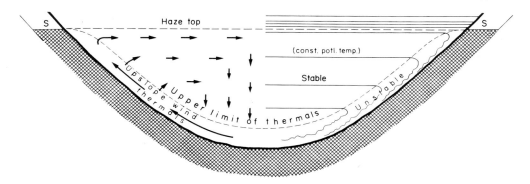

7. *Anabatic Winds* are best developed when the air mass adjacent to the slope is stably stratified. The surfaces of constant potential temperature are then turned over close to a slope heated by sunshine, and thermal convection takes place in a shallow layer—frequently of the order of 100 metres, when the air mass is isothermal but more when its stability is slight. There is a slow subsidence of the air not penetrated by thermals. The right hand half of the diagram shows temperature, the left half the motion.

The upper limit of the anabatic wind is usually set by the mountain tops, or the snow line, for there the upslope wind ceases to be heated. Anabatic winds are often well developed in sunshine below a subsidence inversion which appears to coincide with S because this is the level to which pollution is carried and at which there is a haze top. Because of the warming below the stability is also greater above S than below. (See also **55**.)

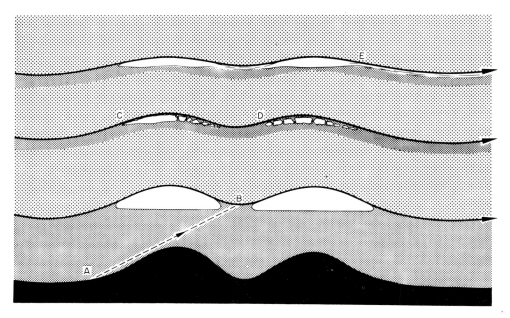

8. *Mountain Waves.* In passing over a hill the horizontal motion of the air is disturbed, though not necessarily according to the simple pattern similar to the ground shape as shown here. Three possible forms of wave cloud are illustrated. The darker layers are assumed to be moister than the others and are lifted above the condensation level in the waves. If the air is stable at the heavy lines the lower cloud will be shaped as shown and a view from A would reveal the arched top of the cloud through the hole at B (**70, 72**).

In the next layer the cloud forms at C as a smooth one but, because of instability, breaks up into cloudlets (**67**); the second cloud at D is then formed in cloudlets which move through the wave (**68**).

The top layer illustrates the possibility that the cloud is glaciated and does not evaporate in the wave trough nor on the downward side at E, and therefore forms a trail (**77**).

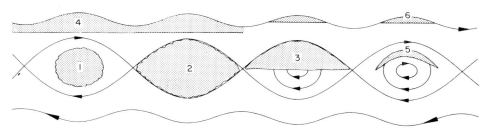

9. *Billows.* The 'cats' eyes' pattern of motion is capable of producing several forms of billows. The whole pattern moves along with the wind, the air above moving faster, that below slower. The billows occur at the level of maximum shear. The closed cells contain the air which circulates, and which moves at the same speed as the pattern.

The possible positions of clouds are shown. Each cloud would occur in the same position in each billow, but only one or two of each is shown here:—
1. Cloud rolls in centres of circulations separated by clear gaps (**61**).
2. Cloud rolls occupying the entire circulation with scarcely any gaps between them (**61**).
3. Cloud rolls in upper parts of circulations only, rounded tops, nearly flat bases (**64**).
4. Layer of cloud above the billows, showing thickening above them (**63**).
5. Eyebrow clouds in the circulations (**62**).
6. Eyebrow clouds above the circulations, showing also how they might be linked by ice cloud.

In many of the illustrations it is not certain which type the cloud is, because the circulations cannot be seen.

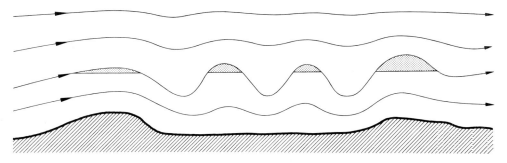

10. *Lee Waves.* On the lee side of a ridge a series of waves may occur, and a series of lee wave clouds may appear (**50, 72**); in this case they are imagined to occur at the top of a moist layer where the air is stable, and the third lee wave is enlarged by happening to occur over another hill.

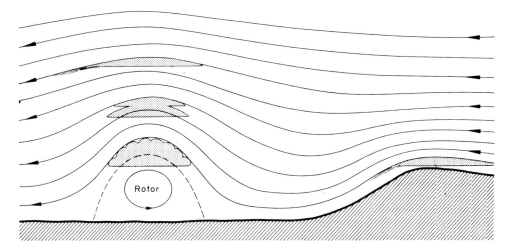

11. *Rotor.* In lee waves of sufficient amplitude rotors are formed under the wave crest. Any cloud which forms in a rotor is extremely turbulent both in fact and in appearance, but the clouds above may be smooth. This diagram illustrates particularly **71**, where above the rotor cloud are smooth wave clouds, the uppermost of which are slightly extended on the downstream side because of glaciation. Over the distant mountain range is a glaciated cloud on the snowcapped mountain, so that it extends down the lee slope for some distance. But the cloud in the rotor mixes into the air just above the rotor and there is no glaciation because none of it is long enough lived. The lee wave may be larger than the wave over the mountain, particularly at high levels and when there is a rotor (**75**).

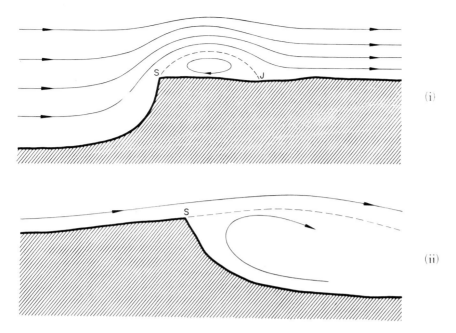

(i)

(ii)

12. *Separation*. The point of separation, S, is the point towards which the wind blows from both directions so that the flow is away from the surface at S. The flow rejoins at the point (J) where the eddy is closed. In the eddy the flow at the surface is reversed. A salient edge is an edge which is so sharp that it almost invariably causes separation. On the top of a cliff, (i), an eddy occurs when it faces the wind and the eddy occurs below the top, (ii), when the wind is the other way. At a sharp ridge, flow over the top induces flow up the lee slope with the consequent formation of a cloud which delineates the streamline from the salient edge (59).

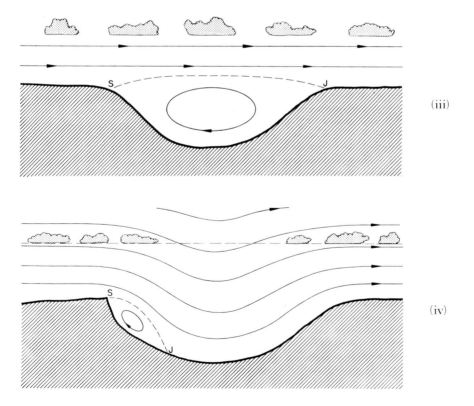

(iii)

(iv)

The flow across a valley may separate, and the streamline from S rejoin on the opposite side, so that the whole valley is filled by an eddy or stagnant air. In such a case (iii), there is no disturbance of the flow above, and cloud formations show no gap over the valley (111). If, however, the flow rejoins on the lee slope, it then follows the valley contour, and there will be evidence in the clouds of the distortion of the flow at higher levels. For example there may be a 'wave hole', or gap in a layer of stratocumulus (70). In (iv) we have also illustrated the possibility that, even though the flow separates at a salient edge on the lee slope it soon rejoins because of the influence of the main stream. Sometimes separation may be prevented by katabatic flow down the lee slope.

40

INDEX AND GLOSSARY

fall speed is just sufficient to remove them from layer clouds. Smaller droplets are carried around by the air motion; larger droplets have fall speeds in excess of the small scale motions in clouds and are called rain. See 15, 120.

Edge of Cloud 45, 93, 103, 104.

Evaporation of Cloud 1-6, 15, 16, 34, 43, 64, 92; by convection 45, 94, 110; of fog 115, 117, 118; see *Wave Hole*.

Evaporation from Land 9, 51, 122.

Fallout Abbreviation for *Water Fallout*, i.e. particles of liquid or frozen water falling from clouds: particles having fall speeds large enough for them to fall out of clouds, i.e. rain, hail, snow, drizzle, etc. 15-20, 24, 25, 28, 41, 80, 85, 87, 95. See also *Mamma, Self-propagating Storm, Warm Rain*.

Fall Speed The terminal speed with which a particle, droplet, etc., would fall in otherwise still air. Cloud droplets acquire their full fall speeds relative to the air in less than a second and larger particles in, at most, a few seconds. See *Magnitudes* (p.xi).

Fallstreaks Streaks of particles forming cirrus by falling through the air. In the case of ice streaks the particles may grow as they fall if the air is supersaturated. Of rain 15; of snow 20; of ice 80-82, 84, 87, 122.

Floccus *Castellanus* (q.v.) which is relatively small, and with a strong shortlived upcurrent, leaving fleecelike trails below the thermals 34.

Fog Arctic smoke 119; dispersion of 115, 118; hill 51, 120; radiation 115, 116; sea 117, 118.

Freezing Level The level above which the air is colder than 0°C. See *Melting Level*, 20.

Front See *Cold Front, Warm Front, Stationery Front*.

Glaciation The process of freezing of supercooled water droplets. A water cloud that becomes an ice cloud is said to have become glaciated. 16-18, 21, 23, 24, 43, 62, 66, 80. See also 71, 76, 77.

Glory The coloured rings caused by diffraction seen round the shadow of the observer on a water cloud: often called the Brocken Spectre: best developed in clouds of uniform drop size 13, 14.

Haidinger's Brushes Quadrants or dumb-bell shaped patches of brown, with more intense blue than in the surrounding sky in between these quadrants, seen by the unfatigued eye centred on the point to which the vision is directed in a highly polarised part of the blue sky. They may equally well be seen by looking through a polarising screen at a source of unpolarised light (e.g. white paper or a cloudy sky). The brushes fade in a few seconds but are renewed if the direction of polarisation or the eye is rotated. In the blue sky the blue quadrants are oriented at right angles to the direction towards the sun. The phenomenon is physiological, and many people claim that they do not see the "brushes".

Halo In particular the circular arcs seen round the sun or moon at 22°. They are produced at the angle of minimum deviation of light passing through two faces of a hexagonal ice prism which are at 60° to one another 89, 99. Rare haloes at other angles (e.g. 46°, 8°) from the sun are occasionally seen, and they are produced by light passing through faces of ice crystals at other angles, but more common are the associated phenomena (q.v.) of the *Mock Sun* and *Parhelic Circle* 88, *Circumzenithal Arc* 106, and *Sun Pillar* 121.

Haze 45, 111. Salt 112: top 109, 110. See also *Crepuscular Rays*.

Heat of Condensation The latent heat released when condensation occurs.

Hill Fog 51, 120.

Ice Arcs Arcs indicating the presence of ice particles in a cloud. See *Circumzenithal Arc, Halo, Mock Sun, Sun Pillar*.

Ice Cloud Cloud composed of ice crystals. An ice anvil is a glaciated anvil cloud. Ice clouds usually become fibrous or mamma in a few minutes except for ice stratus, which is very thick.

Ice Crystals In clouds (recognition of) Frontispiece, 16, 17, 20, 24, 26, 43, 62, 76-85, 113. See also *Halo*.

Ice Evaporation Level The level to which the air must descend in order to evaporate an ice cloud formed by first lifting the air above the condensation level and then glaciating the cloud so formed. It is the level at which during ascent the air becomes just saturated for ice. 76-79, 90, 113. See also *Orographic Cirrus*.

Ice Stratus A glaciated formless layer of cloud 89, 99.

Instability A state in which the air is statically unstable, and therefore undergoing, or liable to undergo, convection.

Inversion A thin stable layer which acts as an upper limit to convection; often visible as a haze top 109, 110, or as the top of a cloud layer 8, 11, 23, 45, 46, 64, 121; Sub cloud inversion 47. See also *Anvil*.

Iridescence The diffraction phenomenon in which colours are separated by the passage of light through a cloud of droplets of more or less uniform size. Close to the sun the colours appear in concentric rings round the sun and a corona is produced; a corona may also be seen round the moon in a similar cloud. At larger angular distances the colours are determined more by the size of the droplets. 105. See also 76.

Jet Stream A strong wind which blows at high levels, the wind above, below, and either side of it being weaker. A jet stream is an ordinary thermal wind (q.v.) and is produced by the strong horizontal temperature gradient at fronts 79, 82, 103, 104.

Katabatic Wind A shallow stream of cold air down a cold hillside, usually less than 10m deep 116.

Lenticular Lens-shaped; usually referring to wave clouds with arched tops 64, 71-75, 86, 91, 93, 97-98, 105; or to pileus clouds 3, 21; or to oval patches of thin cloud viewed from a distance.

Lee Waves Waves formed on the lee side of a mountain in a suitable airstream. The waves are revealed by parallel bars of stationary wave clouds 50, 64, 69, 72, 75, figs. 10, 11.

Mamma Bulbous protuberances on the base of a cloud layer caused by instability or fallout. The individual mamma may be downward thermals produced by cooling of air immediately below the cloud by evaporation of fallout, or by the downward drag (i.e. the weight) of the fallout. 16, 26, 41, 48, 53, 54, 58, 80.

Melting Level The level below which the temperature is above 0°C and at which the melting of frozen fallout begins 20.

Mist 107. This term is used to refer to very tenuous fog, and is distinguished from haze which is produced by dry particles in the air at rather low humidities. Technically a mist is a cloud of condensed liquid particles with very small fall speeds, and is distinguished from a smoke which is composed of solid particles which have condensed in the air.

Mock Sun The bright coloured patch of light seen at the altitude of the sun just outside the 22° halo in ice clouds containing plenty of vertically oriented hexagonal prisms. The distance from the halo increases with the altitude of the sun. 88.

Mother of Pearl Clouds Iridescent clouds: the name is particularly applied to such clouds which occasionally appear high in the stratosphere (at heights of 18-30 km) and therefore shine brightly when the sun has set from the troposphere and the sky is otherwise dark: these clouds are often given this name even when not actually iridescent. 76. See also 105.

Mountains Convection over, Frontispiece, 10, 40, 55-57, 91. See also *Wave Clouds, Orographic Cirrus*.

Nimbostratus A layer of featureless cloud producing fallout most commonly seen at *Warm Fronts* (q.v.).

Orographic Cirrus Cirrus, which is formed in air passing through a wave, which does not evaporate like a water cloud at the lee side of the wave because the air does not descend below its ice evaporation level (q.v.) and so forms a long trail of ice cloud downwind from the wave crest, 66, 76-79, 90, fig. 8.

Parhelic Circle 88.
Parhelion Another name for *Mock Sun* (q.v.).
Pile d'Asseittes A wave cloud having the appearance of a pile of plates, 73, 86, 97-98.
Pileus The wave-like cap cloud formed temporarily when cumulus rises through a stable layer, lifting it above its condensation level 3, 4, 17, 18, 21, 40, fig. 4.
Polarisation The blue sky is most intensely polarised when sunlight reaches the observer after a single scattering, and is best seen in a direction about 100 degrees from the direction of the sun, mainly because of the multiple scattered light received from the sky in other directions, 97-98. Reflected light is also highly polarised and so rainbows 25, cloud bows 27, parhelic circles 88, and sun pillars 121 are more prominently seen through a polarising screen (which excludes all light except that polarised in one direction). See also 80, 104. The direction of polarisation may be detected by the human eye by means of *Haidinger's Brushes* (q.v.).
Pollution 44, 47, 92, 107, 109-111.

Radiation 107; from cloud top 45, 61. See also *Fog*.
Rain 15, 18-20. See also 114, *Fallout, Warm Rain*.
Rain Front 19, 28. See also *Self-propagating Storm*.
Rainbow 25. The primary bow is seen at an angle of 42° from the direction of the observer's shadow (antisolar point) and is formed by a single internal reflection in the raindrops. The secondary bow is at an angle of 51° and is formed by two internal reflections. Supernumerary bows inside the main bow are not seen if there are drops of a wide range of sizes present; but they are brightest when all the drops are of

approximately the same size, and their spacing depends on the drop size. See also 15 and *Cloud Bow*.
Reticular Cloud A thin layer of cloud in which holes have appeared, causing it to have a net-like structure, 48.
Rotor A closed circulation in a wave, usually of large amplitude, in which the air does not move away downstream. The air in the rotor is often very turbulent, especially if there is any cloud in it, 71, 90, fig. 11.

Salient Edge A sharp edge of a mountain, building, or any solid body, at which the flow separates from the surface, 59. See *Separation*.
Scud Fragmentary cloud appearing below the principal condensation level in damper patches of air 31, 32, 51, 114.
Self-propagating Storm 19, 22, 28-30, 41, 95, fig. 6.
Separation The departure of a streamline from the rigid boundary of a stream of fluid. A line on the boundary towards which the flow converges from both sides is called a line of separation, because the particles move along the surface to it and then away from the surface. Separation occurs at salient edges, 59, fig. 12.
Shadows Of aircraft 13; of alto-cloud 86, 99; contrail 74; cumulus over land 10, 42; cumulus over sea 12; of hills 107. See also *Crepuscular Rays*.
Shear A gradient across the direction of a stream, of the stream velocity (this definition is not applicable to curved flow). Most commonly persistent shear in the free atmosphere occurs where the horizontal wind increases or decreases with height, e.g. the thermal wind, and shear is also common in the layers close to the ground because of the drag of the surface. 5, 6, 17, 18, 61-63, 80-82, 92, 103-104, 107, fig. 3. See also *Self-propagating Storm, Streets*.
Showers A shower cloud is a *Cumulonimbus* (q.v.). See *Self-propagating Storm*.
Smoke A cloud of solid particles condensed above a fire, usually composed of unburnt volatile components or products from the fuel. According to this strict definition fire ash particles are not smoke, and the visible components in plumes from many tall chimneys is all ash, dust, or *Mist* (q.v.). 107.
Snow 20, 41, 87, 95.
Spreading out of Cumulus 7, 12, 23, 43, 44, 58. See also 48, 53, *Anvil*.
Squall Line 32.
Stable Stratification The situation in which the potential temperature of the air increases upwards (sometimes called a 'condition of inversion'). A parcel of air displaced vertically in these con-

ditions experiences a buoyancy force towards its original level. 3, 10, 30, 55, 68, 102, 107, 122.
Stable Layer 7, 8, 11, 23, 40, 43, 45, 65. See *Inversion*.
Stationary Front 84, 101.
Strato-cirrus See *Cirrostratus*.
Stratocumulus A layer of cumuliform cloud, the cloudlets often being merged so that the layer is continuous but lumpy and contains appreciable vertical velocities (1 m sec^{-1} or more) within it. Sometimes the cloudlets are separated by clear spaces which are generally narrower than the cloudlets. 12, 45, 46, 50, 65, 102. See also *Water Anvil*, 8.
Stratosphere The layer of stably stratified air, often of fairly uniform temperature, extending from the tropopause up to the base of the warmer layers which begin at about 25 to 30 km (and which are often called the mesosphere). Clouds are very rare in the stratosphere. See 76, *Tropopause*.
Stratus A layer of cloud having neither fibrous nor cumuliform structure 52, 94, 120, 121. See also *Altostratus, Ice Stratus, Cirrostratus*.
Streets Lines of cumulus clouds which usually lie roughly along the direction of the wind, which is frequently also the direction of wind shear. Streets are best formed when the convection is confined to a layer of uniform depth over a large area. Thermals in clear air may be arranged in streets, usually below an inversion, even though none reaches the condensation level and no cloud is formed. The updraughts are much more continuous under streets of clouds than under isolated cumulus. 11, 39, 42, also 91, 113.
Striations Transverse streaks across a band of cirrus, usually caused by shear across the direction of the band. 82, 90.
Subsidence Slow sinking motion over a large area, characteristic of anticyclones 8, 84, and of the cold air behind cold fronts, particularly those moving towards the equator 102-4, or ahead of active fronts 86, 99, or in the neighbourhood of strong upcurrents in convection 11, 47.
Sun Pillar 121.
Sunrise 64, 90, 94, 107-108, 121.
Sunset 54, 62, 68, 76, 77.
Supersaturation Condensation nuclei are so plentiful that for practical purposes the air cannot become saturated with water vapour without cloud being formed. Virtually all excess water vapour is condensed out as cloud. But the air may be supersaturated for ice at temperatures below 0°C, because cloud is not normally formed until the air is made supersaturated for water. See Magnitudes p. xii, *Ice Evaporation Level, Fallstreaks, Orographic Cirrus*.

Thermals Masses of buoyant air rising through their surroundings and becoming diluted by them as they rise Figs. 1-5. Thermals are produced when the air is unstable. If the buoyancy is produced by condensation the thermals are visible as cloud. Castellanus 33-6; small cumulus 55, 57; isolated 24; negative 6, 16, 54; in shear 92. See also *Cumulus, Evaporation by Convection, Mamma.*

Thermal Source A place on the ground from which thermals originate frequently or continuously for some time: a source must be warmer than the surroundings at the same level. Examples are high ground 55, 57 (see also *Mountains*), dry sand and concrete, ripe corn surrounded by green vegetation, power stations, natural and artificial fires. See also 39.

Thermal Wind The shear, or change of wind velocity with height, produced by the earth's rotation in an airstream with a horizontal temperature gradient. The direction of the shear is cyclonically round the cold air or anticyclonically round the warm air. See *Jet Stream.*

Thunderstorm A shower in which lightning is produced 29. The electrical phenomena have no important effect on the form of the cloud.

Tropopause The upper limit of the troposphere, the base of the stratosphere, 21, 26, 41.

Troposphere The lower part of the atmosphere in which clouds are common and in which the weather takes place: it contains nearly three quarters of the total mass of the atmosphere.

Visibility 109-112, in cloud 2.

Warm Front The front boundary of an advancing warm air mass. 29, 82, 85-86, 99-101.

Warm Rain Rain produced in clouds in which there are no ice crystals, occurring most commonly in warmer climates when the temperature at cloud base is 10°C or more 15, 25.

Warm Sector The part of an extratropical cyclone where the warm air mass is present at the earth's surface 118, 120.

Warming by Subsidence Subsidence warms air adiabatically as it sinks to levels of higher pressure; cloud is therefore evaporated by subsidence. If the air is stably stratified the temperature at a fixed altitude is increased by subsidence, and it is this kind of subsidence which produces anticyclonic inversions because the subsidence (and therefore the warming) is less near the ground than higher up 8, 47, 102.

Water Cloud Cloud composed of water droplets, possibly supercooled, but containing no ice crystals.

Water Fallout See *Fallout.*

Wave Cloud Cloud whose shape is determined by wave motions in the air. Wave clouds are commonly in more or less fixed positions relative to the mountains causing the waves. 36, 65, 73, 77-78, 85, fig. 8. See also 2, 16, 37, 52, 86. Castellanus in 34-36; cloudlets in 67, 68; fingers 65, 69; iridescent 105. See *Lee Waves, Orographic Cirrus, Rotor, Whaleback Cloud.*

Wave Hole (or trough) The trough between two waves. Air passing through a trough may have the cloud in it evaporated by the sinking, in which case a hole often appears in a cloud layer 50, 70.

Whaleback Cloud A smooth lenticular wave cloud, 64, 72.

OTHER TITLES OF INTEREST

A Colour Encyclopaedia of Clouds is a comprehensive and unparalleled collection of cloud photographs, 300 in colour and 115 in black and white, with full explanations of the physical and dynamical mechanisms which produce the clouds. Many rare phenomena are shown in colour for the first time, and the book gives the fullest treatment yet accorded to several topics: Contrails, inversions, optical phenomena, waves, thermals, smoke plumes, hurricanes, tornadoes, cyclones, etc., are illustrated by typical clouds: Satellite and radar pictures are included.

A Colour Guide to Clouds is a reference book containing 48 pictures of cloud forms, selected from the **Colour Encyclopaedia of Clouds,** with captions explaining the most important cloudmaking processes. It forms an excellent introduction, in handy pocket form, to a subject of absorbing interest to physicists, geographers, naturalists, yachtsmen, artists and others.

A Colour Panorama of Clouds is a popular presentation of skyscapes, written mainly for airline passengers, to enable them to appreciate the great beauty of the sky. Many dramatic aerial photographs are included.

A Screen Colour Guide to Clouds (A and B) consists of two filmstrips (frames 24 x 36 mm.): A contains pictures 1-26 of "A Colour Guide to Clouds" with two colour diagrams, B contains pictures 27-48 with two colour diagrams. It may be cut up and mounted as separate slides or used as continuous filmstrips for classes and lectures in conjunction with the book.